This Book
Belongs to:

_____

Forward

Hello everybody! Welcome to the Traveling Bear Journeys.

The Journey, *Traveling Bear and the Drive-Through Safari*, emphasizes the importance of finding answers to all of one's questions. Read this journey with your child. At the end, complete the "What's Most Important?" exercise with your child. The purpose of this exercise is to help your child recognize the positive behavioral patterns that are exemplified throughout the journey and motivate your child to go after something special.

Remember, have fun and just find a way to get there!

Visit Traveling Bear at www.travelingbear.com

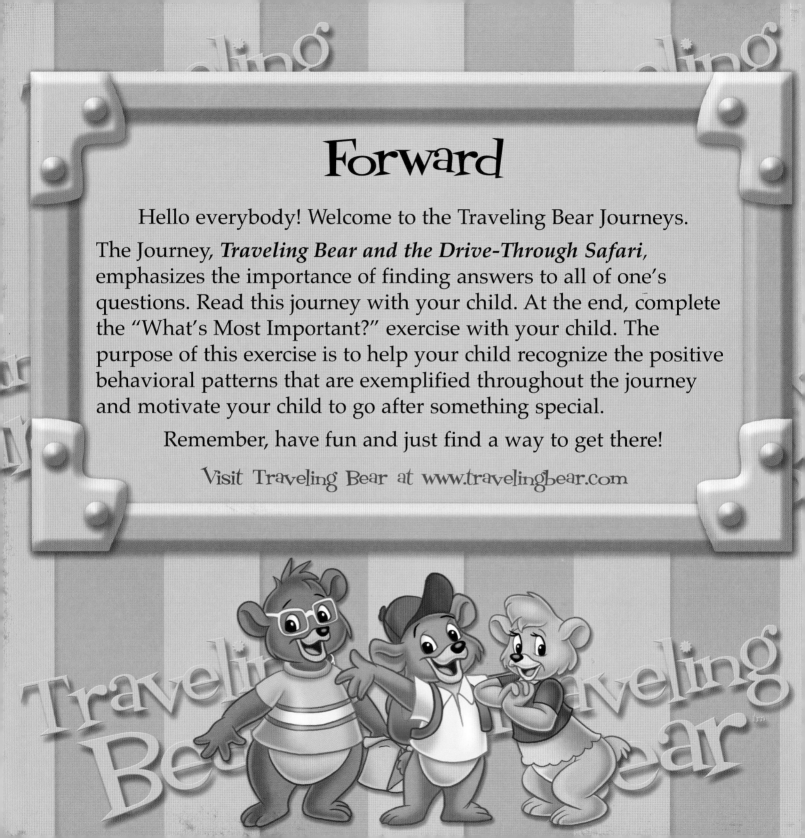

Traveling Bear™ and the Drive-Through Safari

"Finding Answers"

Emma's yellow bus rode through a very special place where all kinds of different animals lived.

As the bus drove down a bumpy road and turned into a cave, Traveling Bear tried really hard not to feel scared.

Soon, the doors of the bus swung open and a bear with a fuzzy mustache climbed inside.

"Welcome!" he said. "I'm your tour guide, Big Sheldon. I have paper and pencils for everyone. You can write down all your questions about the animals you see on our drive-through safari."

As Emma drove down the road, a kangaroo jumped out of the bushes and hopped alongside the bus.

Traveling Bear studied the kangaroo. He had a lot of questions for Big Sheldon. Could the kangaroo jump over the Safari Park wall? Do kangaroos always hop or do they sometimes walk? He was one curious bear!

Next, Traveling Bear wanted to know if the monkeys he saw were able to climb as high as the treetops. And what was in the big shack they passed by? Was that an elephant's trunk peeking out at him?

Traveling Bear wrote down all of his questions until he couldn't write another word. He knew that he would have to be patient and wait for his answers until after the tour.

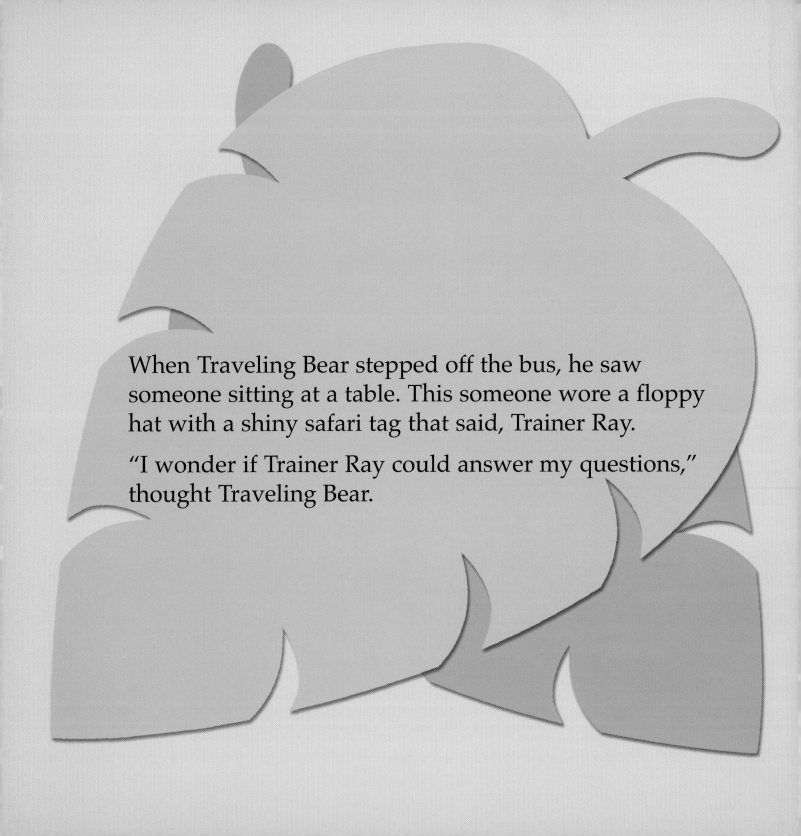

When Traveling Bear stepped off the bus, he saw someone sitting at a table. This someone wore a floppy hat with a shiny safari tag that said, Trainer Ray.

"I wonder if Trainer Ray could answer my questions," thought Traveling Bear.

Traveling Bear went over to ask for help. "I have some questions about the animals in the park," he said.

"Ask away," said Trainer Ray. Then he pulled out a book for Traveling Bear.

"But before you do, maybe you can find the answers to your questions right here."

Traveling Bear took the book and thanked Trainer Ray.

"I know a great place where you'll find more books about animals and lots of other things," said Ray.

"Where?" asked Traveling Bear.

"In the library," said Ray.

At the end of the tour, Sheldon and Emma asked Traveling Bear if he had any questions for them.

"Well," said Traveling Bear. "I did, but I was able to find the answers inside this book."

Sheldon and Emma thought that was great! "You found the answers on your own," Sheldon said. "Now that's what learning is all about!"

Traveling Bear shouted, "Hip-hip hooray! Learning on my own just made my day!"

"Wow! What a day . . .

We all know that if you want good things in life to happen to you,

Here's what you need to do... 1, 2, 1 - 2 - 3

Get out of bed I said, get fed, have bread, just find a way to get there.

Travel to school on a mule, on a bike, take a hike, just find a way to get there.

Let out a moan, sing a tone, talk on the phone, just find a way to get there.

On a boat, on a goat, on a plane or on the train, just find a way to get there.

Forget about your hair, so people take a stare, who cares, just find a way to get there!

Bye. everybody!

What's Most Important?

Read the paragraphs below with your child and help him/her circle the words in each parenthesis that best completes the sentence.

At the beginning of the story, Traveling Bear has an (**easy, hard**) time holding in his questions. He (**shouts out, writes down**) all of his questions because he realizes that (**is, isn't**) the best way to go through the tour. Once the tour is over, Traveling Bear (**waits, looks**) for answers because he (**wants, doesn't want**) to learn more. He meets Trainer Ray, and he learns from him that answers can (**sometimes, never**) be found in a book and that books can be found in a (**cave, library**).

I learned that Traveling Bear (**gives up, keeps plugging away**) at finding answers to all of his questions. The next time that I really want to find out about something that I think can help me, I'm going to be like Traveling Bear and (**quit, just find a way to get there**).